Percents

5-6

Written by
Pamela Jennett and Steve Davis

Editors: Carla Hamaguchi and Jennifer Busby
Production: Karen Nguyen
Cover Designer: Barbara Peterson
Art Director: Moonhee Pak
Project Manager: Collene Dobelmann
Project Director: Betsy Morris

Table of Contents

Introduction

Percents 5–6 contains ready-to-use activity pages to provide students with skill practice. The fun activities can be used to supplement and enhance what you are already teaching in your classroom. Give an activity page to students as independent class work, or send the pages home as homework to reinforce skills taught in class. An answer key is included at the end of the book as a convenient reference.

This book provides activities that will directly assist students in practicing basic skills and concepts. The structure of the book enhances students' learning and enables them to meet new challenges with confidence. The activities in this book progress from simple to more difficult. Because calculating percents relies on a mastery of multiplication and long division, you may decide if your students should use calculators to complete the pages.

Students will receive reinforcement in the following skills:

- Identifying and naming percents
- Finding and ordering equivalent fractions, decimals, and percents
- Determining the percent of a number
- Finding a variable
- Using percents in real-world activities
- Solving equations involving percents

Use *Percents 5–6* to reinforce or extend concepts and skills. "Recharge" skill review with the ready-to-go activities in this book, and give students the power to succeed!

Name _____ Date _____

Parts of a Whole

A percent is another way to name a fraction or a decimal. **Percent** means "out of a hundred." It names the part of a whole.

 = 35%

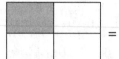 = 25%

Write the percent that is shaded.

1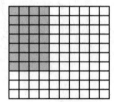

_____

2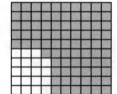

_____

3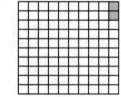

_____

4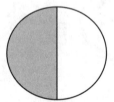

_____

5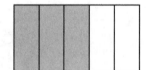

_____

6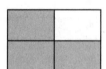

_____

7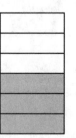

_____

8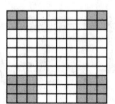

_____

9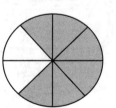

_____

Three Ways to Say It

A percent is another way to name a fraction or a decimal. Percent means "out of a hundred." It names the part of a whole.

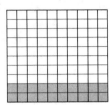

⅕ or 0.20 or 20%

Write a fraction, a decimal, and a percent to indicate the part that is shaded.

 ❶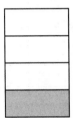

_____

❷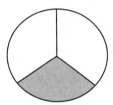

_____

❸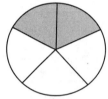

_____

❹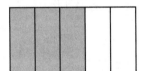

_____

❺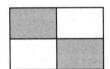

_____

❻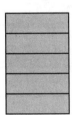

_____

❼

_____

❽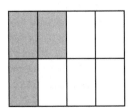

_____

❾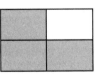

_____

Ratios and Percents

To convert a ratio to a percent, the second term in the ratio must be 100.

Ratio: 4 out of 10	**Ratio**: 3 out of 5

1. Multiply both numbers by ten =
     40 out of **100**
2. Name the Percent = **40%**
	1. Multiply both numbers by 20 =
	     60 out of **100**
	2. Name the Percent = **60%**

Write the percent.

❶ 50 out of 100	❷ 34 out of 100	❸ 98 out of 100
_____	_____	_____
❹ 8 out of 100	❺ 29 out of 100	❻ 100 out of 100
_____	_____	_____
❼ 4 out of 5	❽ 8 out of 25	❾ 49 out of 50
_____	_____	_____
❿ 12 out of 20	⓫ 18 out of 20	⓬ 21 out of 25
_____	_____	_____
⓭ 8 out of 50	⓮ 16 out of 100	⓯ 16.5 out of 25
_____	_____	_____
⓰ 7 out of 10	⓱ 1.5 out of 50	⓲ 3.75 out of 20
_____	_____	_____

Percents • 5–6 © 2007 Creative Teaching Press

What's Missing?

Complete the chart with the missing ratio, fraction, and percent equivalents. Reduce fractions to lowest terms.

Ratio	Fraction	Percent
27 out of 100		
	¹⁶⁄₂₅	
48 out of 100		
		6%
		25%
35 out of 50		
		46%
	¾	
3 out of 5		
		58%

Decimals to Percents

Convert a decimal to a percent by multiplying the decimal by 100.

$$0.5 \times 100 = 50\%$$

Shortcut: Move the decimal two spaces to the right.

$0.5 \longrightarrow 0\ 5\ 0. = 50\%$

$0.25 \longrightarrow 0\ 2\ 5. = 25\%$

1 0.25 =

2 0.5 =

3 0.3 =

4 0.4 =

5 0.6 =

6 0.62 =

7 0.125 =

8 0.8 =

9 0.10 =

10 0.99 =

11 0.32 =

12 0.45 =

13 0.625 =

14 0.725 =

Percents • 5–6 © 2007 Creative Teaching Press

From Decimals to Percents or Back

Convert a decimal to a percent by multiplying the decimal by 100.

$.25 \times 100 = 25\%$

Shortcut: Move the decimal two spaces to the right.

0.5 ⟶ 0 5 0. = 50%

.25 ⟶ 0 2 5. = 25%

Convert a percent to a decimal by dividing the percent by 100.

$$25\% \longrightarrow 100\overline{)25.00}^{.25}$$

Shortcut: Change the % sign to a decimal and move the decimal two spaces to the left.

25% = 2 5.

25. = .2 5

Change each decimal to a percent or each percent to a decimal.

1 30% =

2 0.7 =

3 75% =

4 0.84 =

5 95.5% =

6 0.955 =

7 0.67 =

8 0.96 =

9 99% =

10 0.33 =

11 0.123 =

12 10% =

Percents Greater Than One

Convert a decimal to a percent by multiplying the decimal by 100.

$$1.0 \times 100 = 100\%$$

Shortcut: Move the decimal two spaces to the right.

$$1.25 \longrightarrow 1\,2\,5. = 125\%$$

1 2.25 =

2 3.00 =

3 1.50 =

4 1.75 =

5 1.10 =

6 2.00 =

7 3.25 =

8 2.12 =

9 9.10 =

10 7.99 =

11 5.32 =

12 4.45 =

13 1.625 =

14 10.0 =

One Way or Another

Convert a decimal to a percent by multiplying the decimal by 100.

$$1.25 \times 100 = 125\%$$

Shortcut: Move the decimal two spaces to the right.

$$1.25 \longrightarrow 1\,2\,5. = 125\%$$

Convert a percent to a decimal by dividing the percent by 100.

$$125\% \longrightarrow 100\overline{)125.00}^{\,1.25}$$

Shortcut: Change the % sign to a decimal and move the decimal two spaces to the left.

$$125\% = 1\,2\,5.$$
$$125. = 1.2\,5$$

Change each decimal to a percent or each percent to a decimal.

1 100% =

2 1.0 =

3 5.0 =

4 200% =

5 3.33 =

6 4.56 =

7 1,000% =

8 7.50 =

9 825% =

10 6.49 =

11 9.12 =

12 500% =

Show Three Ways

Find the equivalent decimal and percent for each fraction.

1 $\frac{7}{8}$ = __0.875__ = __87.5%__

2 $\frac{3}{4}$ = _____ = _____

3 $\frac{1}{10}$ = _____ = _____

4 $\frac{5}{8}$ = _____ = _____

5 $\frac{5}{10}$ = _____ = _____

6 $\frac{15}{50}$ = _____ = _____

7 $\frac{7}{7}$ = _____ = _____

8 $\frac{2}{3}$ = _____ = _____

9 $\frac{3}{20}$ = _____ = _____

10 $\frac{4}{5}$ = _____ = _____

11 $\frac{8}{32}$ = _____ = _____

12 $\frac{85}{100}$ = _____ = _____

13 $\frac{2}{5}$ = _____ = _____

14 $\frac{6}{75}$ = _____ = _____

Name _____ Date _____

Finding Larger Conversions

Convert each fraction to a decimal and then to a percent. Round decimals to nearest thousandth. (**Hint:** Change each improper fraction to a mixed number before finding the decimal equivalent.)

1 $1\frac{1}{4} =$ __1.25__ = __125%__

2 $1\frac{1}{5} =$ _____ = _____

3 $4\frac{5}{8} =$ _____ = _____

4 $3\frac{1}{10} =$ _____ = _____

5 $1\frac{8}{32} =$ _____ = _____

6 $1\frac{2}{40} =$ _____ = _____

7 $4\frac{4}{14} =$ _____ = _____

8 $\frac{225}{75} =$ _____ = _____

9 $7\frac{2}{5} =$ _____ = _____

10 $9\frac{4}{5} =$ _____ = _____

11 $\frac{341}{123} =$ _____ = _____

12 $1\frac{7}{10} =$ _____ = _____

13 $5\frac{2}{5} =$ _____ = _____

14 $\frac{150}{25} =$ _____ = _____

Percents • 5–6 © 2007 Creative Teaching Press

Find Equivalents

Find the missing equivalent(s). The first one is done for you

1 ½ = 0.50 = __50%__

2 ⅕ = _____ = 20%

3 _____ = 0.3̄3̄ = 33.3%

4 ½₀ = _____ = 5%

5 ³⁄₁₂ = 0.25 = _____

6 _____ = 0.1 = 10%

7 ⁷⁄₇ = 1 = _____

8 ⅖ = _____ = 40%

9 _____ = 0.15 = 15%

10 ²⁴⁄₃₀ = 0.8 = _____

11 ³⁷⁵⁄₆₀ = _____ = 625%

12 _____ = 0.72 = 72%

13 ⁵⁄₁₂₅ = _____ = _____

14 ³⁶⁄₄₀ = _____ = _____

Percents • 5–6 © 2007 Creative Teaching Press

Name _____ Date _____

Set the Table

Find the equivalent percent, decimal, or fraction to complete the chart. Reduce fractions to lowest terms.

	Percent	Decimal	Fraction
1	50%		
2	25%		
3		0.45	
4			⅓
5		1.0	
6			⅞
7	1%		
8			⅝
9	125%		
10	8%		
11		0.15	
12			1 ½

Convert and Compare

To compare a decimal to a percent, convert the numbers to the same form.

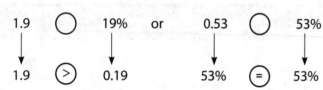

1.9 ◯ 19%   or   0.53 ◯ 53%

1.9 (>) 0.19   53% (=) 53%

Compare the numbers. Write <, >, or = in each circle.

1 14.5% ◯ 0.98

2 1.6 ◯ 6.6%

3 0.333 ◯ 33%

4 0.259 ◯ 29.5%

5 112% ◯ 1.120

6 0.4 ◯ 40%

7 0.55 ◯ 505%

8 24.8% ◯ 0.402

9 0.08 ◯ 9%

10 1.15% ◯ 1.15

11 0.194 ◯ 19.4%

12 0.208 ◯ 28%

More or Less

To compare and order decimals and percents, convert them to the same form.

Write the numbers in order from least to greatest.

1 2.7   27%   0.207   207%   7.2

_____

2 0.65   6.2%   16.5%   1.6   0.59

_____

3 13%   1.3   0.103   3.10   31%

_____

4 49.8   48%   8.04   8%   4.08

_____

5 Place the following numbers on the number line by writing the corresponding letter in each circle.

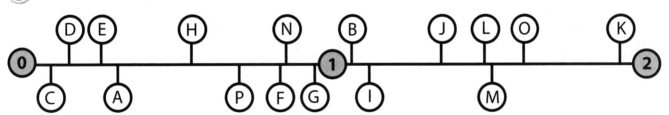

A. 25%   **B.** 101%   **C.** 0.05   **D.** 0.100

E. 19.8%   **F.** 80%   **G.** 0.97   **H.** 0.480

I. 1.06   **J.** 137%   **K.** 1.98   **L.** 1.5

M. 152%   **N.** 0.815   **O.** 1.625   **P.** 63.5%

Percent of a Whole Number

Replace **what** with *n*. ———————————————→ 10% of 45 is what?
10% of 45 is *n*
Replace **is** with =. Convert percent to a decimal. ———→ 10% = $^{10}/_{100}$ = 0.10 of 45 = *n*
Replace **of** with *x*. ———————————————→ 0.10 × 45 = 4.5
10% of 45 is 4.5

Solve.

1 10% of 40

2 20% of 50

3 50% of 150

4 25% of 100

5 30% of 90

6 75% of 200

7 100% of 88

8 60% of 120

9 15% of 65

10 22% of 80

11 9% of 60

12 1% of 70

13 2% of 34

14 55% of 48

Percents • 5–6 © 2007 Creative Teaching Press

What Percent Is It?

Replace **what** with *n*. ⎯⎯⎯⎯⎯⎯⎯⎯⎯⎯⎯⎯⎯⎯⎯⎯→
Replace **is** with =. Replace **is** with =. Convert percent to a decimal. ⎯⎯⎯→
Replace **of** with *x*. ⎯⎯⎯⎯⎯⎯⎯⎯⎯⎯⎯⎯⎯⎯⎯⎯→

10% of 163 is what?
10% of 163 is *n*
$10\% = {}^{10}\!/_{100} = 0.10$ of 163 = *n*
$0.10 \times 163 = 16.3$
10% of 163 is 16.3

Solve.

1 110% of 40

2 28% of 65

3 6% of 128

4 125% of 65

5 98% of 82

6 33% of 68

7 75% of 1

8 112% of 55

9 81% of 32

10 77% of 80

11 28% of 28

12 12% of 54

13 101% of 36

14 62% of 38

Name _____ Date _____

Find the Missing Percent

1. 3 is what percent of 4?

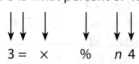

3 =   ×   %   n 4

2. Divide by 4 on each side to isolate the variable.

$$\frac{3}{4} = \frac{4}{4} \times n$$

3. Divide fraction to find the percent.

$$\frac{3}{4} = 75\%$$

Solve to find the missing percents. Round each answer to a whole number.

1 5 is what percent of 10?

2 15 is what percent of 40?

3 6 is what percent of 120?

4 10 is what percent of 80?

5 8 is what percent of 52?

6 33 is what percent of 88?

7 20 is what percent of 20?

8 7 is what percent of 80?

9 81 is what percent of 90?

10 45 is what percent of 50?

11 13 is what percent of 72?

12 90 is what percent of 99?

13 52 is what percent of 72?

14 62 is what percent of 112?

Percents • 5–6 © 2007 Creative Teaching Press

What Is the Missing Percent?

Solve to find the missing percents.

1 1.92 is what percent of 24?

2 26 is what percent of 40?

3 120 is what percent of 480?

4 30.4 is what percent of 95?

5 23.97 is what percent of 47?

6 10.8 is what percent of 135?

7 2.99 is what percent of 23?

8 86.64 is what percent of 114?

9 5.58 is what percent of 62?

10 18 is what percent of 100?

11 68.89 is what percent of 83?

12 35.15 is what percent of 37?

13 9.01 is what percent of 17?

14 98.01 is what percent of 99?

Find the Missing Original Number

Example:	10 is 10% of what?	10% of what? is 10
Replace **is** with =. Change percent to decimal. Replace **what** with *n*. Replace **of** with *x* . **Do the math.**	$10 = 0.10$ of what? $10 = 0.10$ of n $10 = 0.10 \times n$ $\frac{10}{0.10} = \frac{0.10}{0.10} \times n$ $100 = n$	0.10 of what? $= 10$ 0.10 of $n = 10$ $0.10 \times n = 10$ $\frac{0.10}{0.10} \times n = \frac{10}{0.10}$ $n = 100$

Solve to find the missing original number. The first two are done for you.

1 4 is 25% of ____16____
$4 = 25\%$ of n
$4 = .25 \times n$
$\frac{4}{0.25} = \frac{4}{0.25} \times n$
$16 = n$

2 30% of ___100___ is 30
30% of $n = 30$
$30\% \times n = 30$
$\frac{30}{0.30} \times n = \frac{30}{0.30}$
$n = 100$

3 20% of _____ is 10

4 5 is 20% of _____

5 40% of _____ is 32

6 10 is 1% of _____

7 60% of _____ is 48

8 85% of _____ is 51

9 66 is 60% of _____

10 22 is 11% of _____

11 15% of _____ is 3

12 75% of _____ is 30

13 82 is 20% of _____

14 6 is 30% of _____

Percents • 5–6 © 2007 Creative Teaching Press

What Is the Missing Original Number?

Solve to find the missing number.

1 10 is 25% of _____

2 45% of _____ is 450?

3 16% of _____ is 10

4 15 is 36% of _____

5 18% of _____ is 65

6 137.75 is 95% of _____

7 83% of _____ is 187.58

8 48% of _____ is 46.08

9 8.25 is 33% of _____

10 221.52 is 26% of _____

11 29% of _____ is 8.41

12 72% of _____ is 234

13 1.45 is 7.25% of _____

14 509.49 is 81% of _____

Variables with Percents

Use multiplication or division to identify the variable.

Multiplication
Step 1: $42 \times 35\% = n$
Step 2: $42 \times .35 = n$

Step 3: $n = 14.7$

Division
Step 1: $n \times 35\% = 14.7$
Step 2: $n = \frac{14.7}{0.35}$

Step 3: $n = 42$

Solve for each variable.

1 $90\% \times 110 = n$

2 $n\% \times 95 = 14.25$

3 $n \times 18\% = \$52.92$

4 $51\% \times n = 127.5$

5 $n = 19\% \times 600$

6 $n\% \times 150 = 183$

7 $n\% \times \$866.00 = \$199.18$

8 $71\% \times n = \$710.00$

9 $99\% \times n = 767.25$

10 $n = 4\% \times 88$

11 $772.65 = n\% \times 505$

12 $50\% \times n = 341.5$

Percents • 5–6 © 2007 Creative Teaching Press

Find the Unknown

To find an unknown percent or amount, rewrite each problem as an equation. Replace certain words with the corresponding symbols.

Replace **what** with n.   22 is 25% of what number?

Replace **is** with =. $22 = 0.25 \times n$

Replace **of** with x. $\frac{22}{0.25} = n$

                       $88 = n$

                       22 is 25% of 88

Solve. Round answers to the nearest hundredth.

1 What is 8% of 6,019?

2 53.73 is what percent of 199?

3 18.75 is 9% of what number?

4 What is 115% of $95.00?

5 What is 64% of 12.5?

6 $131.04 is 18% of what value?

7 606 is 75% of what number?

8 101 is what percent of 404?

9 What is 26% of $25.95?

10 70.52 is 82% of what value?

Name _____ Date _____

What's the Price?

To find the sales price, multiply the original price by the discount. Subtract the discount from the original price.

original price
$20.00

discount
15%

$20.00 × 0.15 = $3.00 discount

$20.00 − $3.00 = $17.00 sale price

Find each sales price. Round to the nearest penny.

1 — 10% Off!

$30.00

$ _____
sale price

2 — 15% Off!

$118.50

$ _____
sale price

3 — 20% Off!

$99.99

$ _____
sale price

4 — 25% Off!

$365.00

$ _____
sale price

5 — 30% Off!

$110.00

$ _____
sale price

6 — 15% Off!

$159.98

$ _____
sale price

Percents • 5–6 © 2007 Creative Teaching Press

What a Bargain!

Find the sale price for each price tag.

1  $99.00   sale price _____

2  $6.00   sale price _____

3  $19.99   sale price _____

4  $1,000.00   sale price _____

5  $68.68   sale price _____

6  $550.00   sale price _____

7  $15.00   sale price _____

8  $108.50   sale price _____

9  $9.99   sale price _____

10  $25.00   sale price _____

11  $110.00   sale price _____

12  $99.00   sale price _____

Name _____ Date _____

How Much Off?

Find the discount percent. First, find the difference between the original price and the discount price. Divide the difference by the original price to get the discount percent, and round to the nearest tenth.

Was
$105.00

Now
$49.98

$$\begin{array}{r} \$105.00 \\ -\ \ 49.98 \\ \hline 55.02 \end{array} \quad = \quad \frac{55.02}{105.00} \quad = \quad 0.524 \quad or \quad 52.4\% \ discount$$

Find the **percent** of each discount. Round answers to the nearest tenth.

1

Original Price
$69.99

On Sale!
$55.99

_____ % off

2

Was
$153.50

Now!
$107.45

_____ % off

3

Was
$6,995.00

Your Cost
$5,050.00

_____ % off

4

List Price
$500.00

Sale Price
$395.00

_____ % off

5

Original Price
$42.50

You Pay
$14.96

_____ % off

6

Pre-Sale Price
$299.90

On Sale Now
$249.22

_____ % off

What's My Discount?

1. Find the discount amount.
2. Divide the difference by the original price.

$1,220.00
−   999.00
$ 221.00

$\frac{221.00}{1220.00}$ = 0.18114

or

≈18.1% discount

~~$1,220.00~~
$999.00

Find the **percent** of each discount off the sale price. Round to the nearest tenth.

1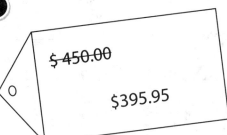

~~$ 450.00~~

$395.95

_____% off

2

~~$ 850.99~~

$525.98

_____% off

3

~~$ 90.00~~

$79.02

_____% off

4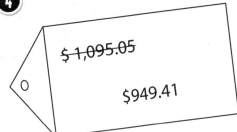

~~$ 1,095.05~~

$949.41

_____% off

5

~~$ 695.00~~

$650.00

_____% off

6

~~$ 1,776.00~~

$1,332.00

_____% off

Name _____ Date _____

Comparison Shopping

First, add up the original cost of the items. Then, find the sale price of each item. Finally, add up the sale prices of the items to compare.

Find the discounted price for each item. Add up each list to find who spent the most money and who saved the most money.

Cammie's Shopping List	Original price	Sale price
1 markers 20% off	$14.99	_____
2 notebook 20% off	$5.00	_____
3 can of nuts 15% off	$5.69	_____
4 hair clips 18% off	$9.50	_____
5 box of tissues 5% off	$1.89	_____
6 backpack 10% off	$21.99	_____
7 jacket 16% off	$29.50	_____
8 running shoes 32% off	$35.99	_____
totals:	_____	_____

Tony's Shopping List	Original price	Sale price
9 watercolors 10% off	$14.99	_____
10 juice boxes 8% off	$3.99	_____
11 book 17% off	$5.95	_____
12 pencil box 20% off	$7.89	_____
13 sweatshirt 12% off	$25.99	_____
14 running shoes 32% off	$35.05	_____
15 notebook 20% off	$6.50	_____
16 music CD 12% off	$14.99	_____
totals:	_____	_____

17 What was Cammie's total cost after the discounts were taken? _____

18 What was Cammie's total savings? _____

19 What was Tony's total cost after the discounts were taken? _____

20 What was Tony's total savings? _____

21 Who saved the most money? _____

Percents • 5–6 © 2007 Creative Teaching Press

Name _____ Date _____

Who Saved the Most?

These signs show the sale items at a department store. Find what each person paid for each item on his or her list. Find the total each spent. Round to the nearest penny or percent when determining amounts.

What Ana Bought:	**What Jack Bought:**	**What Todd Bought:**
2 dresses $30.00 each _____	1 watch $25.00 _____	3 shirts $22.50 _____
3 tank tops $12.50 each _____	1 backpack $39.99 _____	2 T-shirts $11.99 each _____
2 T-shirts $9.99 each _____	2 shirts $22.50 each _____	3 pairs of shorts $14.50 _____
1 pair of shoes $29.00 _____	2 pairs of pants $32.00 each _____	1 pair of pants $21.50 _____
2 boxes of colored pencils $5.00 each _____	2 pairs of boots $38.00 each _____	2 three-ring binders $5.99 each _____
3 pairs of jeans $19.00 each _____	1 wallet $9.99 _____	2 pairs of soccer shoes $34.00 each _____
❶ Ana's total bill: _____	❷ Jack's total bill: _____	❸ Todd's total bill: _____

❹ Who spent the most money? _____

❺ About what percent more was his or her bill than each of the other two bills? _____ _____

Name _____ Date _____

Tip the Waiter

The total check is $42.50. The tip is 15%. What is the total amount after adding the tip?	
To find **tip** total:	$42.50 × 15% = tip $42.50 × 0.15 = $6.375 (round to $6.38)
To find **new** check total:	original total + tip = new total $42.50 + 6.38 = $48.88

Look at each guest check, and then read the questions below to calculate the tip and/or total amount. (Remember to round to the nearest penny.)

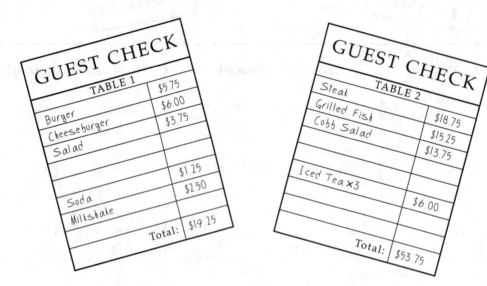

1 A 10% tip for Table #1 would be _____.

2 A 15% tip for Table #2 would be _____.

3 Add a 20% tip to Table #2. The total amount would be _____.

4 Add a 15% tip to Table #1. The total amount would be _____.

Name _____ Date _____

Your Total Check

Look at each guest check and then read the questions below to calculate the tip and/or the total amount. (Remember to round to the nearest penny when finding the tip amount.)

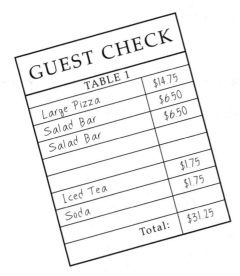

1 Add a 14% tip to Table #1. What would be the total paid? _____

2 A 15% tip for Table #2 would be _____.

3 Add an 18% tip to Table #2. What would be the total paid? _____

4 Add a 25% tip to Table #1. What would be the total paid? _____

Percents • 5–6 © 2007 Creative Teaching Press

Name _____ Date _____

Sales Tax Totals

The receipt is $42.50. The tax is 7.25%. What is the total amount after adding the tax?

To find the **tax** total:	$42.50 × 7.25% = tax $42.50 × 0.0725 = $3.0812 (round to $3.08)
To find **new** receipt total:	original total + tax = new total $42.50 + $3.08 = $45.58 total

Look at each sales receipt and then read the questions below to calculate the tax and/or the total amount.

Mall Store Receipt #1

Dress............................$52.45

Shirt.............................$24.00

Subtotal: $76.45

Tax: 7.25%

Total: _____

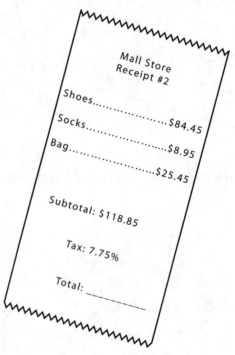

Mall Store Receipt #2

Shoes............................$84.45

Socks............................$8.95

Bag...............................$25.45

Subtotal: $118.85

Tax: 7.75%

Total: _____

1 What is the dollar amount of the tax for Mall Store Receipt #1? _____

2 What is the dollar amount of the tax for Mall Store Receipt #2? _____

3 The total amount with tax of Mall Store Receipt #1 is _____.

4 The total amount with tax of Mall Store Receipt #2 is _____.

Percents • 5–6 © 2007 Creative Teaching Press

Sales Tax in a State

Look at each sales receipt, and then read the questions below to calculate the tax and/or the total amount.

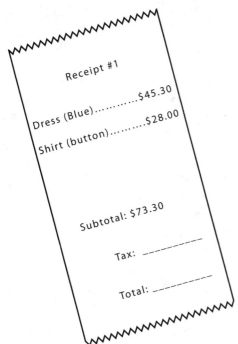

Receipt #1

Dress (Blue)...........$45.30

Shirt (button)........$28.00

Subtotal: $73.30

Tax: _ _ _ _ _ _ _

Total: _ _ _ _ _ _ _

Receipt #2

Shoes.................$79.45

Socks..............$5.95

Belt.................$12.35

Belt.................$13.10

Subtotal: $110.85

Tax: _ _ _ _ _ _

Total: _ _ _ _ _ _

1 In Hawaii, the sales tax is 4%. What is the tax for Receipt #1 in Hawaii? What is the total?

2 The state of Kansas has a 5.3% sales tax. What is the tax for Receipt #2 in Kansas?

3 Arkansas has a sales tax of 6%. What would the total be for Receipt #1 in Arkansas?

4 What would the total be for Receipt #2 if you lived in Kansas?

Fractions of a Circle Graph

A circle graph can show percents of a whole.

 $\frac{50}{100}$ = 50% $\frac{30}{100}$ = 30% $\frac{20}{100}$ = 20%

Remember that all of the fractions in a circle graph must add up to 100/100 or 1/1.

Read the information below to correctly label each part of the circle graph.

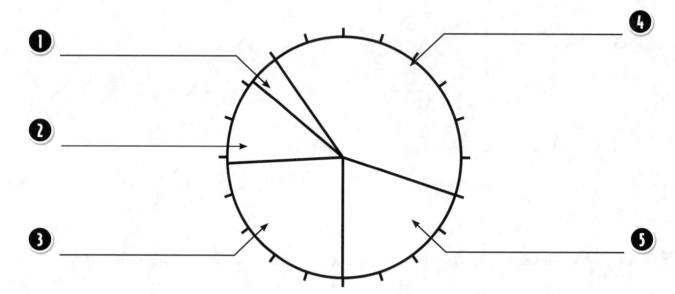

A total of 25 people were asked to name their favorite pet. Of those, 10 people said a dog was their favorite. Another 3 chose a bird. Exactly 5 chose a reptile, such as a snake. Another 6 named a cat as their favorite. The remaining person said she preferred fish.

Write the fraction and percent that shows each pet preference. Reduce fractions to lowest terms.

6 dog _____ _____   **7** bird _____ _____

8 reptile _____ _____   **9** cat _____ _____

10 fish _____ _____

Name _____ Date _____

A Piece of the Pie

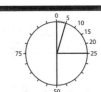

A circle graph, or pie chart, is divided into sectors or parts, each displaying the size of some related piece of information. Circle graphs are used to display the sizes of parts that make up a whole. A circle graph can be divided into 100 equal parts, or percents.

Use each circle graph to answer the questions.

Lunches at Wilson School

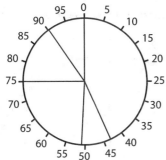

A total of 387 students were surveyed.

2 Find the number of votes for each item. Round to the nearest whole number.

hot dogs _____

pizza _____

tacos _____

spaghetti _____

hamburgers _____

4 Use the percents in Problem 3 to find out how many of each flower were planted. Total should equal 166.

dutch iris _____

daffodil _____

crocus _____

tulip _____

hyacinth _____

1 Read the survey results below. Find the matching percents on the circle graph and label students' choices.

hot dogs 10%

hamburgers 15%

pizza 24%

spaghetti 8%

tacos 43%

3 Use the graph below to find the percent of each bulb planted. Total should equal 100%.

dutch iris _____

daffodil _____

crocus _____

tulip _____

hyacinth _____

Bulbs Planted in Community Garden

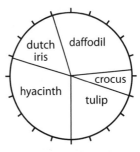

166 bulbs planted

Percents • 5–6 © 2007 Creative Teaching Press

Make a Percent Circle Graph

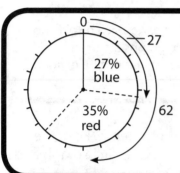

A box of 100 marbles had 27 blue, 35 red, and 38 white marbles.
Find the percent of each marble. Make sure all the percents add up to 100.

1. Start at 0. Count clockwise 27% to mark the first sector.

2. Add 35% to 27% (the first sector's percent) to mark the next sector.

3. Continue around the circle until all the sectors are marked. The remaining sector is 38%.

4. Check your math to see if this is correct.

The park rangers took a count of the types of trees in the park. Out of 200 trees, they counted 48 pines, 38 oaks, 14 maples, 26 hemlocks, 30 cedars, and 44 spruces.

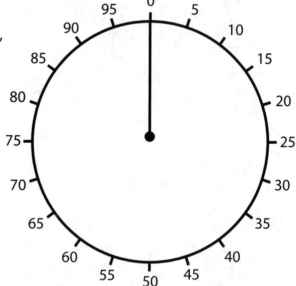

Find the percent of each tree. Use the information to complete the circle graph.

1 pine _____

2 oak _____

3 maple _____

4 hemlock _____

5 cedar _____

6 spruce _____

Story Problems Using Percents

Solve the problems.

1 Julie and Terri went shopping. Julie bought a pair of shorts for $24.95 and a tank top for $15.95. The tank top was on sale for 10% off the regular price. What did Julie pay?

2 Terri bought shorts for $34.45, a T-shirt for $15.50, and sandals for $45.00. If Terri spent more than $50, she would get a 25% discount. What did Terri pay?

3 Paula and Steve went out to dinner and had a wonderful meal. The bill came to $146.85. The service was great, so they wanted to give a 20% tip. What was the total Paula and Steve paid?

4 Your family went on vacation to Florida. While you were at the beach, you bought some ice cream. In Florida, the sales tax is 6%. Your ice cream was $1.25. How much did you have to pay the cashier?

Work It Out

Solve the problems.

1 The Davis family went to a rodeo-style barbeque dinner. It was $25 for each adult and $15 for each child. There were two adults and three kids. If Mr. Davis gave an 18% tip, what would be the total he paid the waiter?

2 Yesterday was the school election. There were 4 students running for president. A total of 658 students voted. The winner received 36% of the vote. The first runner-up received 28% of the vote. If the third runner-up received 16% of the vote, what was the percentage for the second runner-up? How many students voted for the second runner-up? (Note: You will need to round the total votes per student.)

3 In the election above, how many votes did each student receive?

4 Jeremy and his dad went to the sporting goods store. His dad wanted to buy golf shoes and golf balls. He had $75.00 to spend. The shoes were $55.95. The golf balls were $6 for a box of three. If the tax was 5%, how many boxes of golf balls could Jeremy's dad get?

Girls' Volleyball Stats

Western Conference 2007 Wins and Losses

	Vikings	Romans	Tigers	Warriors	Huskies
Wins	5	8	4	7	1
Losses	5	2	6	3	9
Games Played	10	10	10	10	10

Answer the questions based on the chart.

1 What percent of the games did the Vikings win?

2 What percent of the games did the Romans win?

3 What percent of the games did the Tigers lose?

4 Which team had the lowest percentage of wins? What was it?

5 What is the percentage difference between the first-place and second-place teams?

Name _____ Date _____

Basketball Stats

The Eagles' Free Throws for the 2006–2007 Season

	Robbie	Luis	Sam	Nick	David
Free Throws Attempted	86	55	42	37	15
Free Throws Made	52	34	35	12	8

Answer the questions based on the chart.

Find the percent of free-throw shots made out of the free throws attempted by each player. Round each answer to a whole number.

1 Robbie _____   **2** Luis _____   **3** Sam _____

4 Nick _____   **5** David _____

6 Who had the best free-throw percentage? _____

7 Find the percent of free-throw shots made out of the free throws attempted <u>by the team as a whole</u>.

8 The free-throw shots that Robbie made were what percent of the <u>team's</u> total free throws <u>attempted</u>?

9 The free-throw shots that Luis made were what percent of the <u>team's</u> total free throws <u>made</u>?

Percents • 5–6 © 2007 Creative Teaching Press

Name _____ Date _____

What's Your Grade?

Grades are based on percentages. A certain percentage determines a certain grade.

$\dfrac{\text{Number of correct answers}}{\text{Total number possible}}$ = percent score

To find the percent score for 18 problems correct out of 20 problems:

$^{18}\!/_{20} = 0.90$ or 90%

A 90%–100%
B 80%–89%
C 70%–79%
D 60%–69%

Find the percent score for each. Use the chart to determine the letter grade.

1 The weekly spelling test has 20 words. You spell 17 of them right.

What is your percent score? _____   What is your letter grade? _____

2 You take a test with 40 questions. You get 27 problems correct.

What is your percent score? _____   What is your letter grade? _____

3 A math test has 25 problems. You miss 2.

What is your percent score? _____   What is your letter grade? _____

4 There are 50 points possible on a math test. You get 38 points.

What is your percent score? _____   What is your letter grade? _____

Use what you have learned to find the answers.

5 You get 84% on your social studies report. There are 120 points possible.

How many points did you
get correct for your report? _____   What is your letter grade? _____

6 There are 160 problems on a science quiz. You miss 5% of the problems.

How many problems
did you get correct? _____   What is your score and letter grade? _____ _____

Name _____ Date _____

Making the Grade

Report card grades are often based on an average of scores from tests, reports, and assignments.

$$\frac{\text{Sum of all scores}}{\text{Total number of scores}} = \text{average}$$

$$\frac{98\% + 66\% + 87\% + 88\% + 92\%}{5 \text{ scores}} = \frac{431}{5} = 86.2\% = 86\%$$

Using the grading scale to the right, 86.2% would be a B on a report card.

A 90%–100%
B 80%–89%
C 70%–79%
D 60%–69%
F 59% and below

Find the average percent score for each subject. Round all percents to a whole number. Write the report card grade.

Subject	Average Score	Report Card Grade
1 Science 85%, 78%, 92%, 95%, 69%		
2 Math 98%, 85%, 78%, 100%, 95%, 95%, 79%		
3 Reading 100%, 95%, 67%, 78%, 77%, 99%		
4 Spelling 100%, 100%, 95%, 90%, 95%, 100%, 80%, 90%		
5 Social Studies 85%, 96%, 62%, 75%, 55%		
6 Writing 76%, 82%, 71%, 89%, 77%, 82%		

Percents · 5–6 © 2007 Creative Teaching Press

Add or Subtract Percents

First find the percents in parentheses. Then add or subtract to solve for *n*.

1 (50% of 96) + (20% of 85) = *n*

2 (15% of 120) − (8% of 50) = *n*

3 *n* = (25% of 168) + (25% of 84)

4 (660 × 10%) + (550 × 90%) = *n*

5 *n* = (561 × 37%) + (17% of 93)

6 *n* = (9% of 7,890) − (6% of 604)

7 (100% of 1056) − (10% of 9,960) = *n*

8 (405 × 15%) + (10 × 22%) = *n*

9 (88 × 24%) + (96 × 31%) = *n*

10 *n* = (95% of 612) + (5% of 216)

11 (11% of 2,981) − (6% of 590) = *n*

12 (64 × 64%) − (33 × 33%) = *n*

13 *n* = (75% of 200) + (30% of 350)

14 *n* = (562 × 5%) + (55% of 975)

Answer Key

Parts of a Whole (page 4)
1. 28%
2. 81%
3. 2%
4. 50%
5. 60%
6. 75%
7. 50%
8. 26%
9. 75%

Three Ways to Say It (page 5)
1. ¼, 0.25, 25%
2. ⅓, 0.33, 33.3%
3. ⅖, 0.40, 40%
4. ⅗, 0.60, 60%
5. 2/4 or ½, 0.50, 50%
6. 5/5 or 1, 1.00, 100%
7. ⅔, 0.66, 66.6%
8. ⅜, 0.375, 37.5%
9. ¾, 0.75, 75%

Ratios and Percents (page 6)
1. 50%
2. 34%
3. 98%
4. 8%
5. 29%
6. 100%
7. 80%
8. 32%
9. 98%
10. 60%
11. 90%
12. 84%
13. 16%
14. 16%
15. 66%
16. 70%
17. 3%
18. 18.75%

What's Missing? (page 7)

Ratio	Fraction	Percent
27 out of 100	²⁷⁄₁₀₀	27%
16 out of 25	¹⁶⁄₂₅	64%
48 out of 100	¹²⁄₂₅	48%
6 out of 100	³⁄₅₀	6%
25 out of 100	¼	25%
35 out of 50	⁷⁄₁₀	70%
46 out of 100	²³⁄₅₀	46%
3 out of 4	¾	75%
3 out of 5	⅗	60%
58 out of 100	²⁹⁄₅₀	58%

Decimals to Percents (page 8)
1. 25%
2. 50%
3. 30%
4. 40%
5. 60%
6. 62%
7. 12.5%
8. 80%
9. 10%
10. 99%
11. 32%
12. 45%
13. 62.5%
14. 72.5%

From Decimals to Percents or Back (page 9)
1. 0.30
2. 70%
3. 0.75
4. 84%
5. 0.955
6. 95.5%
7. 67%
8. 96%
9. 0.99
10. 33%
11. 12.3%
12. 0.10

Percents Greater Than One (page 10)
1. 225%
2. 300%
3. 150%
4. 175%
5. 110%
6. 200%
7. 325%
8. 212%
9. 910%
10. 799%
11. 532%
12. 445%
13. 162.5%
14. 1,000%

One Way or Another (page 11)
1. 1.00
2. 100%
3. 500%
4. 2.00
5. 333%
6. 456%
7. 10.00
8. 750%
9. 8.25
10. 649%
11. 912%
12. 5.00

Show Three Ways (page 12)
1. 0.875 = 87.5%
2. 0.75 = 75%
3. 0.10 = 10%
4. 0.625 = 62.5%
5. 0.50 = 50%
6. 0.30 = 30%
7. 1.0 = 100%
8. $0.6\overline{6}$ = 66.6%
9. 0.15 = 15%
10. 0.80 = 80%
11. 0.25 = 25%
12. 0.85 = 85%
13. 0.40 = 40%
14. 0.08 = 8%

Finding Larger Conversions (page 13)
1. 1.25 = 125%
2. 1.20 = 120%
3. 4.625 = 462.5%
4. 3.10 = 310%
5. 1.25 = 125%
6. 1.05 = 105%
7. 4.286 = 428.6%
8. 3.00 = 300%
9. 7.40 = 740%
10. 9.80 = 980%
11. 2.77 = 277%
12. 1.70 = 170%
13. 5.40 = 540%
14. 6.00 = 600%

Find Equivalents (page 14)
1. 50%
2. 0.20
3. 1/3
4. 0.05
5. 25%
6. 1/10
7. 100%
8. 0.40
9. 15/100 or 3/20
10. 80%
11. 6.25
12. 72/100 or 36/50 or 18/25
13. 0.04 = 4%
14. 0.9 = 90%

Set the Table (page 15)

Percent	Decimal	Fraction
50%	0.50	½
25%	0.25	¼
45%	0.45	⁹⁄₂₀
33.3%	$0.3\overline{3}$	⅓
100%	1.0	¹⁄₁
87.5%	0.875	⅞
1%	0.01	¹⁄₁₀₀
62.5%	0.625	⅝
125%	1.25	1¼
8%	0.08	²⁄₂₅
15%	0.15	³⁄₂₀
150%	1.50	1½

Convert and Compare (page 16)

1. <
2. >
3. >
4. <
5. =
6. =
7. <
8. <
9. <
10. <
11. =
12. <

More or Less (page 17)

1.	0.207	27%	207%	2.7	7.2
2.	6.2%	16.5%	0.59	0.65	1.6
3.	0.103	13%	31%	1.3	3.10
4.	8%	48%	4.08	8.04	49.8

5.

Percent of a Whole Number (page 18)

1. 4
2. 10
3. 75
4. 25
5. 27
6. 150
7. 88
8. 72
9. 9.75
10. 17.6
11. 5.4
12. 0.7
13. 0.68
14. 26.4

What Percent Is It? (page 19)

1. 44
2. 18.2
3. 7.68
4. 81.25
5. 80.36
6. 22.44
7. 0.75
8. 61.6
9. 25.92
10. 61.6
11. 7.84
12. 6.48
13. 36.36
14. 23.56

Find the Missing Percent (page 20)

1. 50%
2. 38%
3. 5%
4. 13%
5. 15%
6. 38%
7. 100%
8. 9%
9. 90%
10. 90%

11. 18%
12. 91%
13. 72%
14. 55%

What Is the Missing Percent? (page 21)

1. 8%
2. 65%
3. 25%
4. 32%
5. 51%
6. 8%
7. 13%
8. 76%
9. 9%
10. 18%
11. 83%
12. 95%
13. 53%
14. 99%

Find the Missing Original Number (page 22)

1. 16
2. 100
3. 50
4. 25
5. 80
6. 1,000
7. 80
8. 60
9. 110
10. 200
11. 20
12. 40
13. 410
14. 20

What Is the Missing Original Number? (page 23)

1. 40
2. 1,000
3. 62.5
4. $41.6\overline{6}$
5. $361.1\overline{1}$
6. 145
7. 226
8. 96
9. 25
10. 852
11. 29
12. 325
13. 20
14. 629

Variables with Percents (page 24)

1. $n = 99$
2. $n = 15\%$
3. $n = \$294.00$
4. $n = 250$
5. $n = 114$
6. $n = 122\%$
7. $n = 23\%$
8. $n = \$1,000.00$

9. $n = 775$
10. $n = 3.52$
11. $n = 153\%$
12. $n = 683$

Find the Unknown (page 25)

1. $n = 481.52$
2. $n = 27\%$
3. $n = 208.33$
4. $n = \$109.25$
5. $n = 8$
6. $n = \$728.00$
7. $n = 808$
8. $n = 25\%$
9. $n = \$6.75$
10. $n = 86$

What's the Price? (page 26)

1. $27.00
2. $100.72
3. $79.99
4. $273.75
5. $77.00
6. $135.98

What a Bargain! (page 27)

1. $89.10
2. $5.40
3. $17.99
4. $750.00
5. $51.51
6. $412.50
7. $12.75
8. $92.22
9. $8.49
10. $16.75
11. $73.70
12. $66.33

How Much Off? (page 28)

1. 20%
2. 30%
3. 27.8%
4. 21%
5. 64.8%
6. 16.9%

What's My Discount? (page 29)

1. 12%
2. 38.2%
3. 12.2%
4. 13.3%
5. 6.5%
6. 25%

Comparison Shopping (page 30)

1. $11.99
2. $4.00
3. $4.84
4. $7.79
5. $1.80
6. $19.79
7. $24.78

8. $24.47
9. $13.49
10. $3.67
11. $4.94
12. $6.31
13. $22.87
14. $23.83
15. $5.20
16. $13.19
17. $99.46
18. $25.09
19. $93.50
20. $21.85
21. Cammie

Who Saved the Most? (page 31)
1. Ana — $51.00, $30.75, $16.38, $26.10, $8.00, $41.61, $173.84
2. Jack — $22.00, $33.99, $36.00, $46.72, $68.40, $8.49, $215.60
3. Todd — $54.00, $19.18, $31.75, $15.69, $9.58, $61.20, $191.40
4. Jack
5. 19%; 11%

Tip the Waiter (page 32)
1. $1.93
2. $8.06
3. $64.50
4. $22.14

Your Total Check (page 33)
1. $35.63
2. $4.53
3. $35.64
4. $39.06

Sales Tax Totals (page 34)
1. $5.54
2. $9.21
3. $81.99
4. $128.06

Sales Tax in a State (page 35)
1. $2.93, $76.23
2. $5.88
3. $77.70
4. $116.73

Fractions of a Circle Graph (page 36)
1. fish
2. bird
3. cat
4. dog
5. reptile
6. $2/5 = 40\%$
7. $3/25 = 12\%$
8. $1/5 = 20\%$
9. $6/25 = 24\%$
10. $1/25 = 4\%$

A Piece of the Pie (page 37)
1.

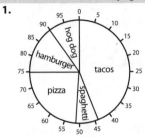

2. hot dogs—39 votes, pizza—93 votes, tacos—166 votes, spaghetti—31 votes, hamburgers—58 votes
3. (Responses may vary but should equal 100%) dutch iris 16%, daffodil 28%, crocus 7%, tulip 20%, hyacinth 29%
4. (Responses may vary but should equal 166) dutch iris 27, daffodil 46, crocus 12, tulip 33, hyacinth 48

Make a Percent Circle Graph (page 38)
1. pine = 24%
2. oak = 19%
3. maple = 7%
4. hemlock = 13%
5. cedar = 15%
6. spruce = 22%

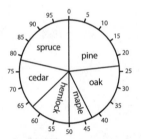

Story Problems Using Percents (page 39)
1. $39.31
2. $71.21
3. $176.22
4. $1.33

Work It Out (page 40)
1. $112.10
2. 20%; 132 students
3. winner—237; 1st runner-up—184; 2nd runner-up—132; 3rd runner-up—105
4. two boxes

Girls' Volleyball Stats (page 41)
1. 50%
2. 80%
3. 60%
4. Huskies, 10%
5. 10% difference between the Romans and the Warriors

Basketball Stats (page 42)
1. Robbie, 60%
2. Luis, 62%
3. Sam, 83%
4. Nick, 32%
5. David, 53%
6. Sam
7. 60%
8. 22%
9. 24%

What's Your Grade? (page 43)
1. 85%, B
2. 68%, D
3. 92%, A
4. 76%, C
5. 101 points, B
6. 152; 95%, A

Making the Grade (page 44)
1. $419 \div 5 = 84\%$, B
2. $630 \div 7 = 90\%$, A
3. $516 \div 6 = 86\%$, B
4. $750 \div 8 = 94\%$, A
5. $373 \div 5 = 75\%$, C
6. $477 \div 6 = 80\%$, B

Add or Subtract Percents (page 45)
1. $(48) + (17) = 65$
2. $(18) - (4) = 14$
3. $(42) + (21) = 63$
4. $(66) + (495) = 561$
5. $(207.57) + (15.81) = 223.38$
6. $(710.1) - (36.24) = 673.86$
7. $(1{,}056) - (996) = 60$
8. $(60.75) + (2.2) = 62.95$
9. $(21.12) + (29.76) = 50.88$
10. $(581.4) + (10.8) = 592.2$
11. $(327.91) - (35.4) = 292.51$
12. $(40.96) - (10.89) = 30.07$
13. $(150) + (105) = 255$
14. $(28.1) + (536.25) = 564.35$